Based on the best-selling keyboard method by I

THE COMPLE

KEYBOARD PLAYER

15 Showstoppers

Wise Publications
part of The Music Sales Group
London/New York/Paris/Sydney/Copenhagen/Berlin/Madrid/Tokyo

Published by
Wise Publications
8/9 Frith Street, London W1D 3JB, UK

Exclusive Distributors:
Music Sales Limited
Distribution Centre, Newmarket Road,
Bury St Edmunds, Suffolk IP33 3YB, UK.
Music Sales Pty Limited
120 Rothschild Avenue, Rosebery, NSW 2018, Australia.

This book © Copyright 2005 Wise Publications,
a division of Music Sales Limited.
Order No. AM983455
ISBN 1-84609-182-9

Compiled by Nick Crispin.
Music arranged by Paul Honey.
Music processed by Paul Ewers Music Design.
Cover photograph courtesy of Robert Eric/Corbis Sygma.
Printed in the United Kingdom by
Printwise (Haverhill) Limited, Haverhill, Suffolk.

Your Guarantee of Quality
As publishers, we strive to produce every book
to the highest commercial standards.
This book has been carefully designed to minimise awkward
page turns and to make playing from it a real pleasure.
Particular care has been given to specifying acid-free, neutral-sized paper
made from pulps which have not been elemental chlorine bleached.
This pulp is from farmed sustainable forests and was produced with special
regard for the environment. Throughout, the printing and binding have been
planned to ensure a sturdy, attractive publication which should give years of enjoyment.
If your copy fails to meet our high standards, please inform us and
we will gladly replace it.

www.musicsales.com

Master Chord Chart

C
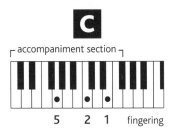

Cm
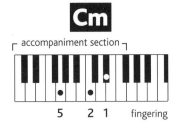

C7
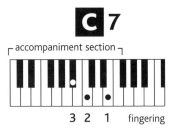

Db(C#)
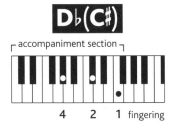

Db(C#)m
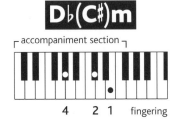

Db(C#)7
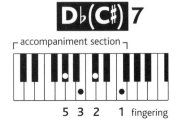

D
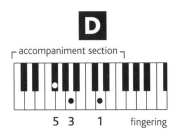

Dm
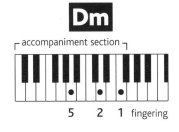

D7
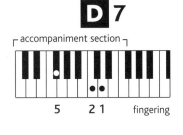

Eb(D#)
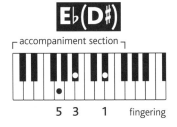

Eb(D#)m
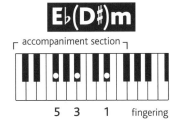

Eb(D#)7
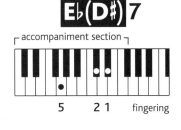

E
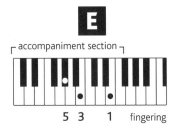

Em
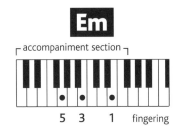

E7
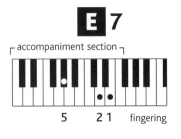

F
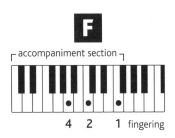

Fm
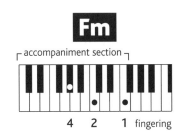

F7
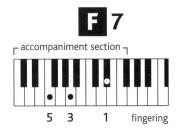

Master Chord Chart

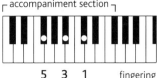 **Gb(F#)**
accompaniment section
5 3 1   fingering

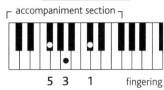 **Gb(F#)m**
accompaniment section
5 3 1   fingering

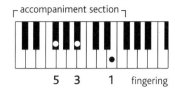 **Gb(F#)7**
accompaniment section
5 3 1   fingering

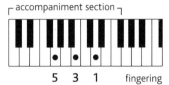 **G**
accompaniment section
5 3 1   fingering

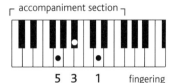 **Gm**
accompaniment section
5 3 1   fingering

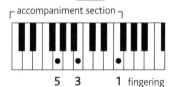 **G7**
accompaniment section
5 3 1   fingering

 **Ab(G#)**
accompaniment section
4 2 1   fingering

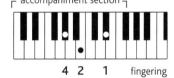 **Ab(G#)m**
accompaniment section
4 2 1   fingering

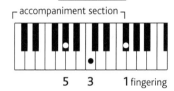 **Ab(G#)7**
accompaniment section
5 3 1 fingering

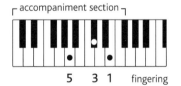 **A**
accompaniment section
5 3 1   fingering

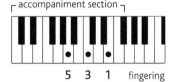 **Am**
accompaniment section
5 3 1   fingering

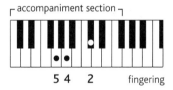 **A7**
accompaniment section
5 4 2   fingering

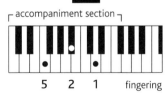 **Bb**
accompaniment section
5 2 1   fingering

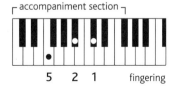 **Bbm**
accompaniment section
5 2 1   fingering

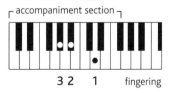 **Bb7**
accompaniment section
3 2 1   fingering

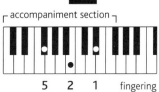 **B**
accompaniment section
5 2 1   fingering

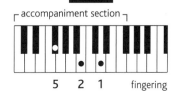 **Bm**
accompaniment section
5 2 1   fingering

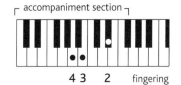 **B7**
accompaniment section
4 3 2   fingering

5

All I Ask Of You

Music by Andrew Lloyd Webber
Lyrics by Charles Hart

Voice: **Flute**
Rhythm: **Ballad**
Tempo: **Gently** ♩ = 70

No more talk of dark-ness, for-get these wide-eyed fears, I'm

here, no-thing can harm you, my words will warm and calm you.

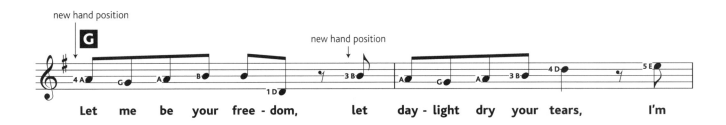

Let me be your free-dom, let day-light dry your tears, I'm

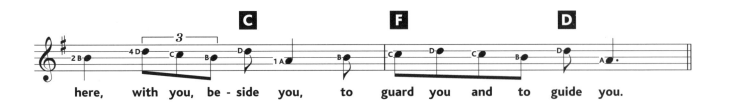

here, with you, be-side you, to guard you and to guide you.

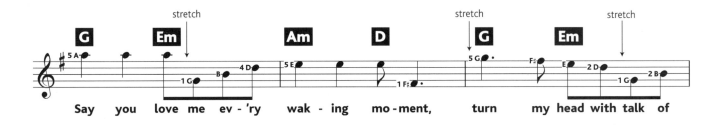

Say you love me ev-'ry wak-ing mo-ment, turn my head with talk of

sum - mer - time.   Say   you   need   me   with   you

now   and   al - ways,   pro - mise   me   that   all   you   say   is   true;

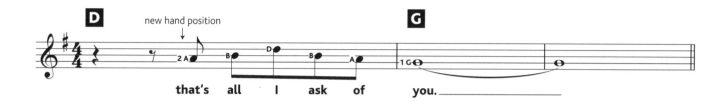

that's   all   I   ask   of   you. _____

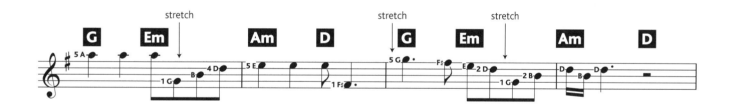

A - ny - where   you   go,   let   me   go

too;   love   me,   that's   all   I   ask   of   you.

Music by Andrew Lloyd Webber
Lyrics by Tim Rice

Voice: **Clarinet**
Rhythm: **16 beat**
Tempo: **Quite slow** ♩ = 64

I

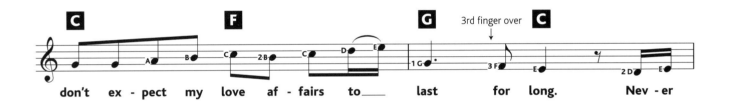

don't ex - pect my love af - fairs to____ last for long. Nev - er

fool my - self that my dreams will come true.

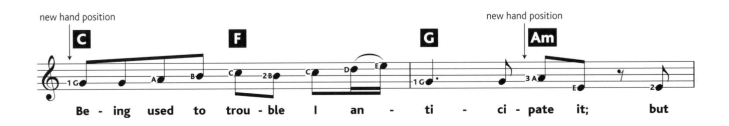

Be - ing used to trou - ble I an - ti - ci - pate it; but

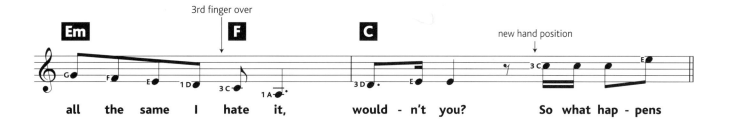

all the same I hate it, would - n't you? So what hap - pens

now? So what hap - pens now? Where am I go -

-ing to? Where am I go - ing to?

So what hap - pens now? So what hap - pens

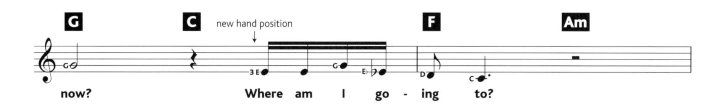

now? Where am I go - ing to?

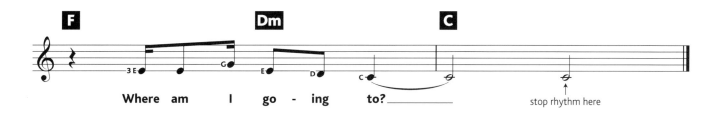

Where am I go - ing to?

As If We Never Said Goodbye

Music by Andrew Lloyd Webber
Lyrics by Don Black & Christopher Hampton

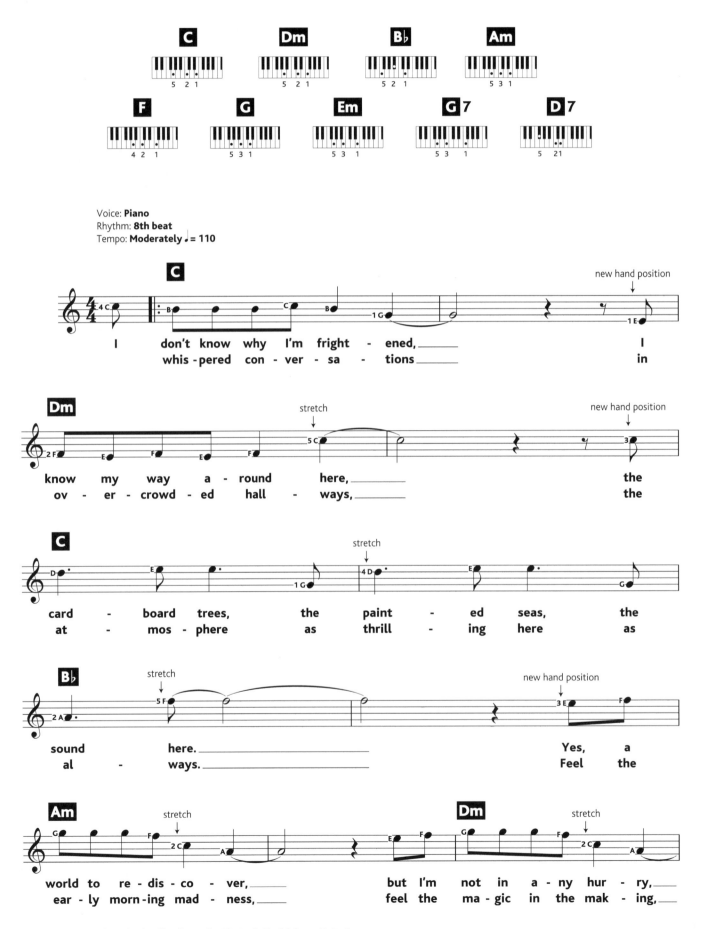

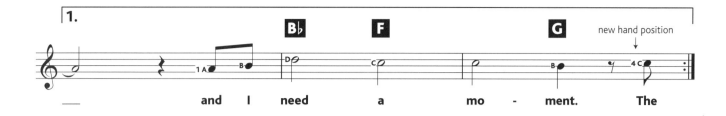

and I need a mo - ment. The

Why, ev-'ry-thing's as if we nev - er said good -

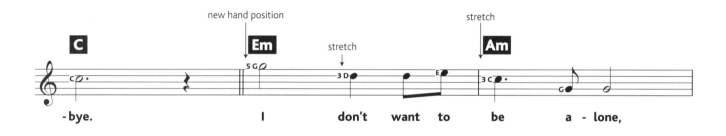

- bye. I don't want to be a - lone,

that's all in the past. This world's wait - ed

long e - nough, I've come home at last. The

whis-pered con - ver - sa - tions _____ in ov - er - crowd - ed hall - ways,_

so much to say, not just to-day but

al - ways._____ We'll have ear - ly morn-ing mad - ness,___

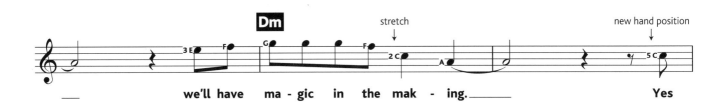

___ we'll have ma - gic in the mak - ing._____ Yes

ev - 'ry-thing's as if we nev - er said good - bye._____

Oh please don't ev - er, ev - er

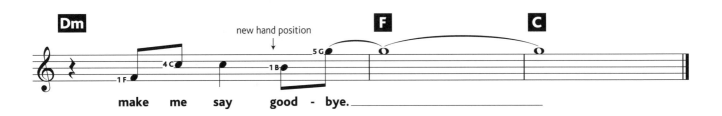

make me say good - bye._____

Can't Help Lovin' Dat Man

Words by Oscar Hammerstein II
Music by Jerome Kern

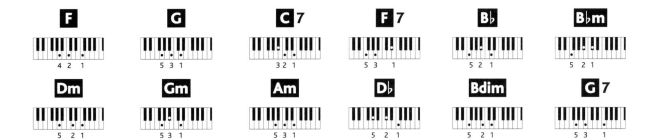

Voice: **Clarinet**
Rhythm: **Swing**
Tempo: **Moderately** ♩ = 100
Synchro start: **On**

Oh lis - ten sis - ter, I love my Mis - ter man, and I

can't tell you why.__ Dere ain't no rea - son why I should love dat

man._____ It must be sum - pin'

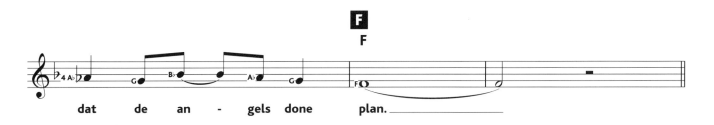

dat de an - gels done plan._____

Fish got to swim, ____ birds got to fly, ____

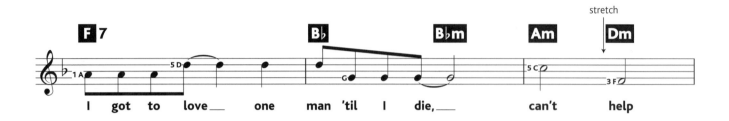

I got to love ___ one man 'til I die, ____ can't help

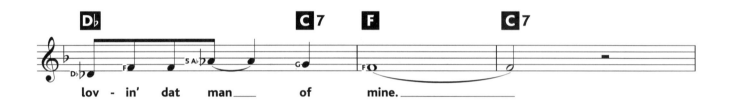

lov - in' dat man ___ of mine. _____

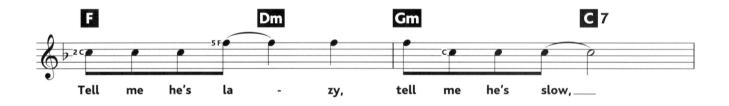

Tell me he's la - zy, tell me he's slow, ____

tell me I'm cra - zy, may - be I know, _ can't help

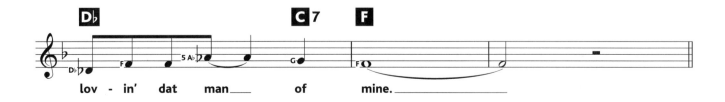

lov - in' dat man ___ of mine. _____

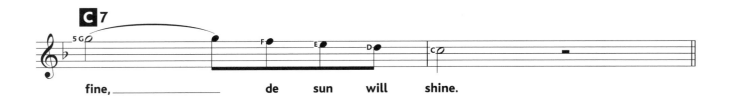

15

Music by Andrew Lloyd Webber
Lyrics by Tim Rice

Voice: **Flute**
Rhythm: **Waltz**
Tempo: **Quite slow** ♩ = 102
Synchro start: **On**

Close ev - 'ry door to me, hide all the world from me,

bar all the win - dows and shut out the light.

Do what you want with me, hate me and laugh at me,

dark - en my day - time and tor - ture my

night. If my life were im - por - tant I would

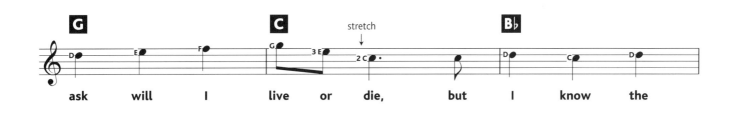

ask will I live or die, but I know the

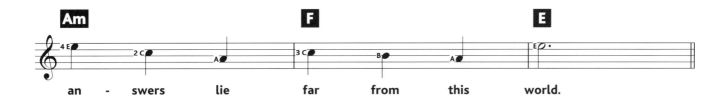

an - swers lie far from this world.

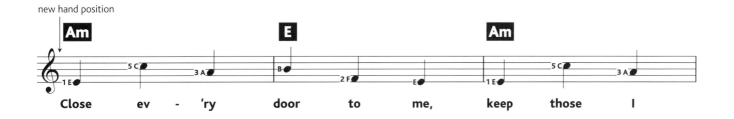

Close ev - 'ry door to me, keep those I

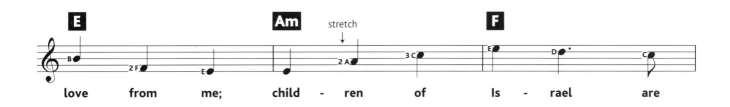

love from me; child - ren of Is - rael are

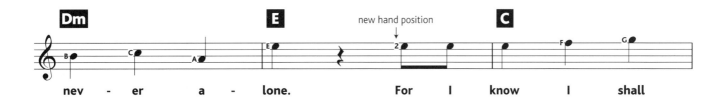

nev - er a - lone. For I know I shall

find my_____ own peace of mind, for

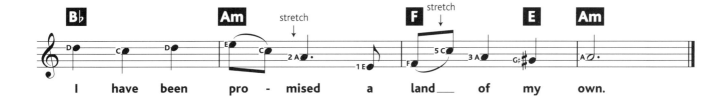

I have been pro - mised a land___ of my own.

17

Do-Re-Mi

Words by Oscar Hammerstein II
Music by Richard Rodgers

Voice: **Piano**
Rhythm: **8th beat**
Tempo: **Moderately** ♩ = 120
Synchro start: **On**

Doe, a deer, a fe-male deer, ray, a drop of gold-en

sun. Me, a name I call my-self,

far, a long, long way to run. Sew, a nee-dle pull-ing

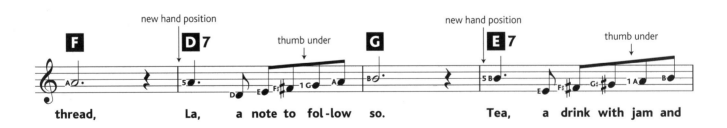

thread, La, a note to fol-low so. Tea, a drink with jam and

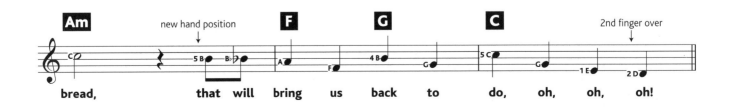

bread, that will bring us back to do, oh, oh, oh!

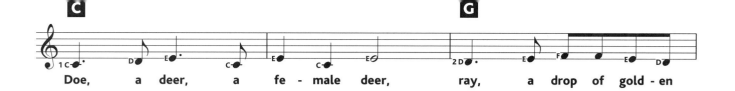

Doe, a deer, a fe - male deer, ray, a drop of gold - en

new hand position

sun. Me, a name I call my - self,

thumb under

far, a long, long way to run. Sew, a nee - dle pull - ing

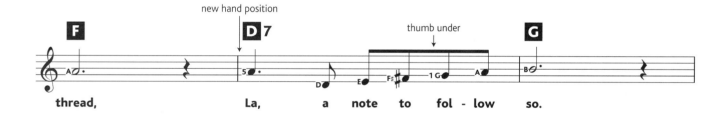

new hand position

thumb under

thread, La, a note to fol - low so.

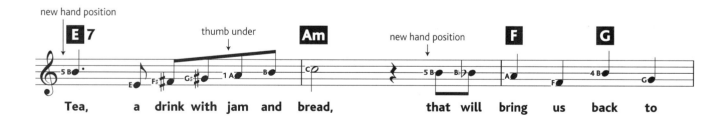

new hand position

thumb under

new hand position

Tea, a drink with jam and bread, that will bring us back to

thumb under

doe! Do - Re - Mi - Fa - So - La - Ti - Do!

Music by Claude-Michel Schönberg
Lyrics by Alain Boublil & Herbert Kretzmer

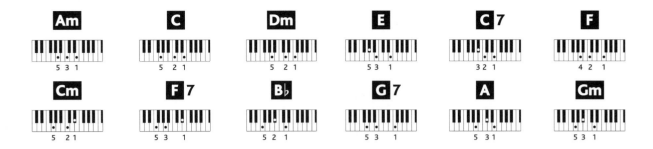

Voice: **Guitar**
Rhythm: **Ballad**
Tempo: ♩ = 90

There's a grief that can't be spo-ken, _____ there's a pain goes on and

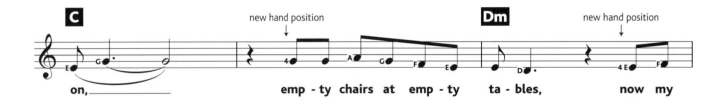

on, _____ emp-ty chairs at emp-ty ta-bles, now my

friends are dead and gone. Here they talked of re-vo-

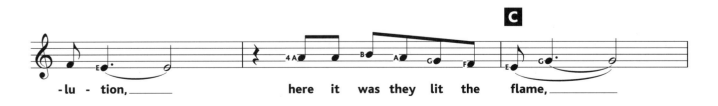

-lu-tion, _____ here it was they lit the flame, _____

here they sang a - bout to - mor - row and to -

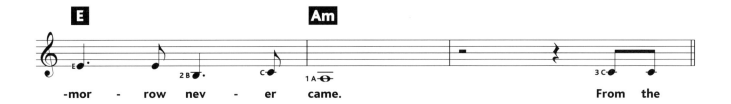

-mor - row nev - er came. From the

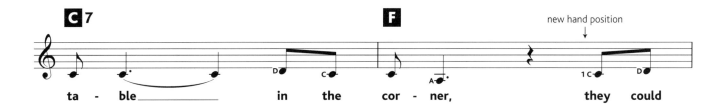

ta - ble_____ in the cor - ner, they could

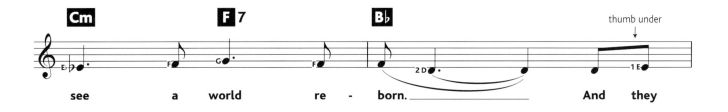

see a world re - born._____ And they

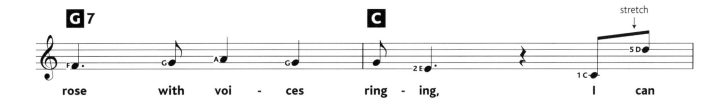

rose with voi - ces ring - ing, I can

hear them now, the ve - ry words that they had

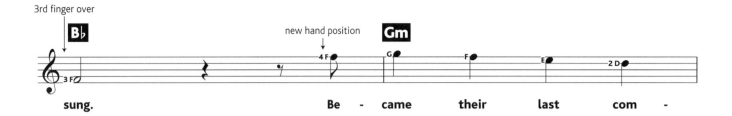

sung.   Be - came   their   last   com -

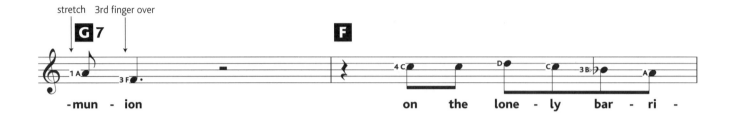

-mun - ion   on   the   lone - ly   bar - ri -

-cade   at   dawn.   Oh   my   friends, my   friends   for -

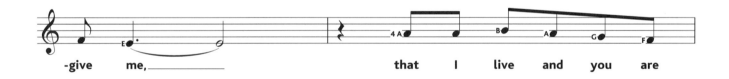

-give   me, _____   that   I   live   and   you   are

gone, _____   there's   a   grief   that   can't   be

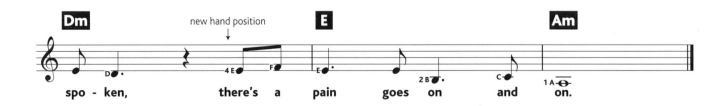

spo - ken,   there's   a   pain   goes   on   and   on.

I Don't Know How To Love Him

Music by Andrew Lloyd Webber
Words by Tim Rice

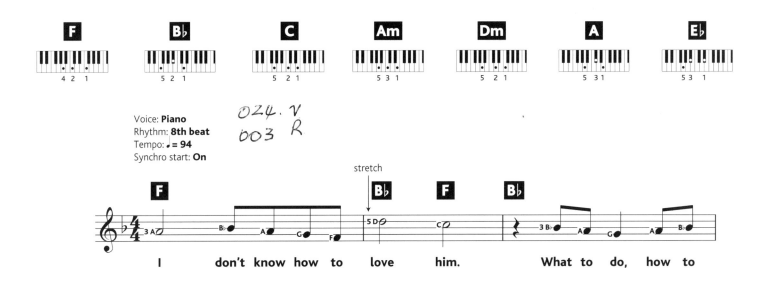

Voice: **Piano**
Rhythm: **8th beat**
Tempo: ♩ = **94**
Synchro start: **On**

024. V
003 R

I don't know how to love him. What to do, how to

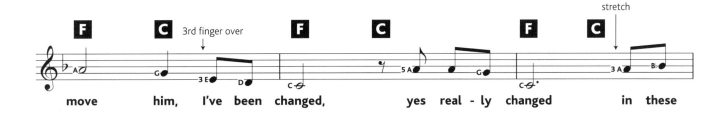

move him, I've been changed, yes real - ly changed in these

past few days when I've seen my - self, I seem like some - one

else. I don't know how to take this,

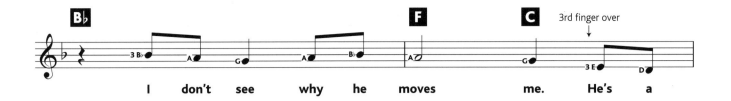

I don't see why he moves me. He's a

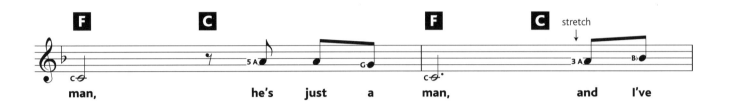

man, he's just a man, and I've

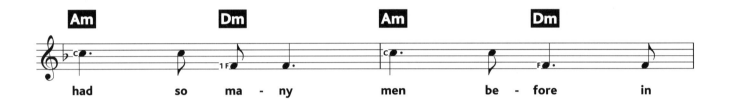

had so ma - ny men be - fore in

ve - ry ma - ny ways, he's just one more.

Should I bring him down, should I scream and shout, should I speak of

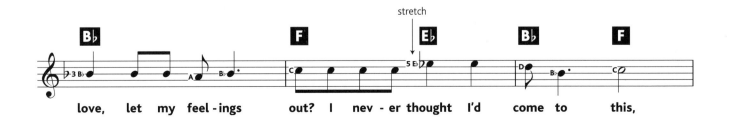

love, let my feel - ings out? I nev - er thought I'd come to this,

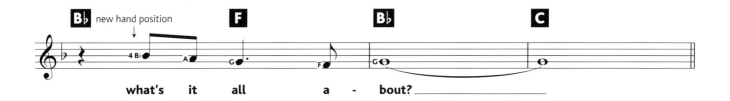

what's it all a - bout? _____

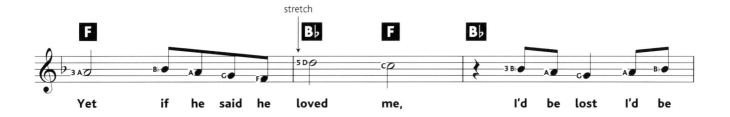

Yet if he said he loved me, I'd be lost I'd be

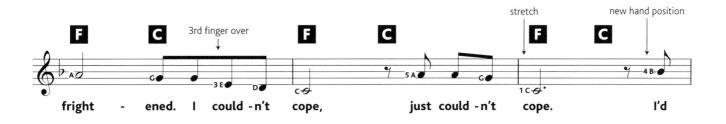

fright - ened. I could -n't cope, just could -n't cope. I'd

turn my head, I'd back a - way, I

would - n't want to know, he scares me

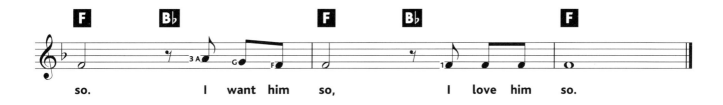

so. I want him so, I love him so.

If I Were A Rich Man

Words by Sheldon Harnick
Music by Jerry Bock

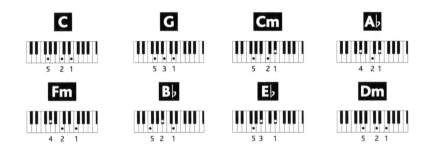

Voice: **Clarinet**
Rhythm: **8th beat**
Tempo: **Moderately** ♩ = 100
Synchro start: **On**

If I were a rich man, di - dle dee - dle di - dle

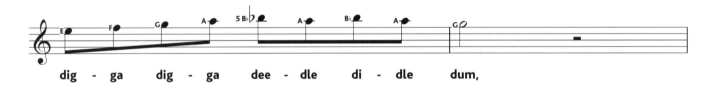

dig - ga dig - ga dee - dle di - dle dum,

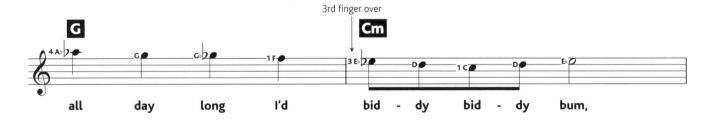

all day long I'd bid - dy bid - dy bum,

if I were a wealth - y man.

Would - n't have to work hard, di - dle dee - dle di - dle

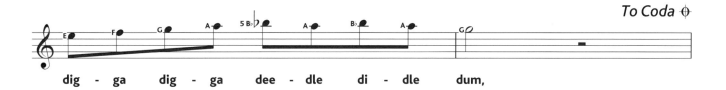

dig - ga dig - ga dee - dle di - dle dum,

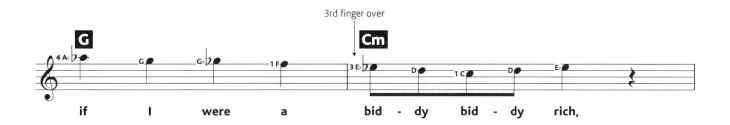

if I were a bid - dy bid - dy rich,

dig - ga dig - ga dee - dle di - dle man. I'd build a

big tall house with rooms by the do - zen, right in the mid - dle of the

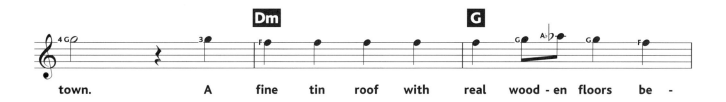

town. A fine tin roof with real wood - en floors be -

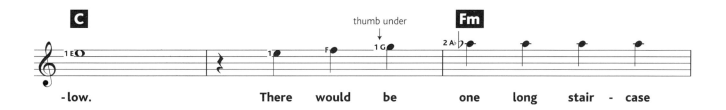

- low. There would be one long stair - case

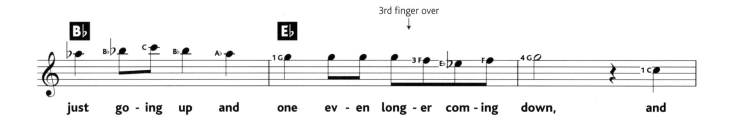

just go - ing up and one ev - en long - er com - ing down, and

D.C. al Coda

one more lead - ing no - where just for show.

⊕ *CODA*

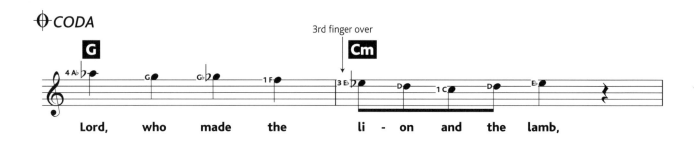

Lord, who made the li - on and the lamb,

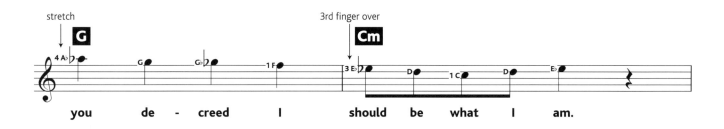

you de - creed I should be what I am.

Would it spoil some vast e - ter - nal plan if I were a

wealth - y man.

Leaning On A Lamp Post

Words & Music by Noel Gay

Voice: **Clarinet**
Rhythm: **Swing**
Tempo: **Moderately** ♩ = 120
Synchro start: **On**

Lean - ing on a lamp, may - be you think I look a

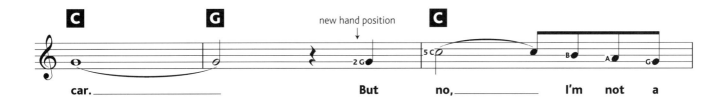

tramp, or you may think I'm hang - ing round to steal a

car. _____ But no, _____ I'm not a

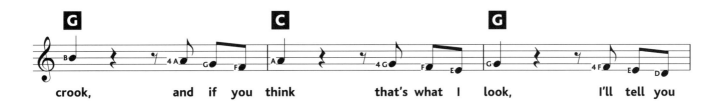

crook, and if you think that's what I look, I'll tell you

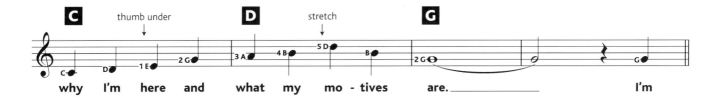

why I'm here and what my mo - tives are. _____ I'm

lean - ing   on   a   lamp - post   at   the   cor - ner   of   the   street,   in   case   a

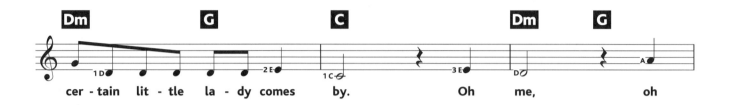

cer - tain   lit - tle   la - dy   comes   by.   Oh   me,   oh

my,   I   hope   that   lit - tle   la - dy   comes   by.   I

don't   know   if   she'll   get   a - way,   she   does - n't   al - ways   get   a - way,   but

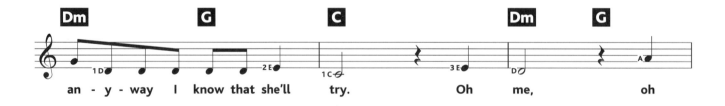

an - y - way   I   know   that   she'll   try.   Oh   me,   oh

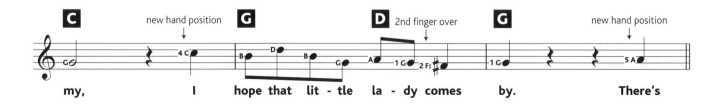

my,   I   hope   that   lit - tle   la - dy   comes   by.   There's

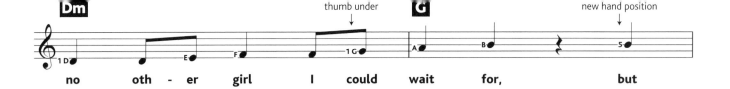

no oth - er girl I could wait for, but

this one I'd break an - y date for. I won't have to ask what she's

late for, she'd nev - er leave me flat, she's not a girl like that. She's

ab - so - lute - ly won - der - ful and mar - vel - lous and beau - ti - ful and

an - y - one can un - der - stand why I'm lean - ing on a lamp - post at the

cor - ner of the street, in - case a cer - tain lit - tle la - dy comes by.

Words & Music by Billy Austin & Louis Jordan

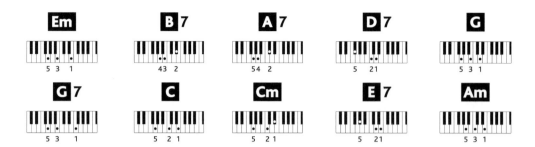

Voice: **Jazz guitar**
Rhythm: **Swing**
Tempo: **Moderately** ♩ = 118
Synchro start: **On**

Is you is, or is you ain't my ba - by?_____

The way you're act - ing late - ly makes me

doubt. You is still my ba - by,

ba - by?_____ Seems my flame in

your heart done gone out. A

wo - man is a crea - ture that has al - ways been

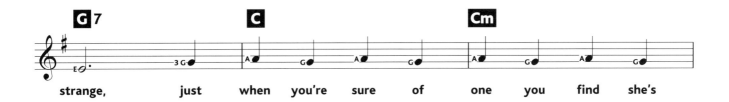

strange, just when you're sure of one you find she's

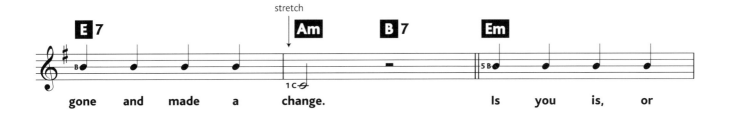

gone and made a change. Is you is, or

is you ain't my ba - by?_____ may - be ba - by's

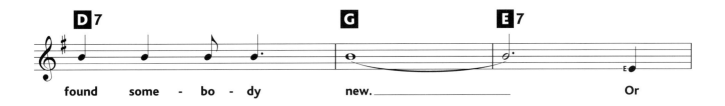

found some - bo - dy new._____ Or

is my ba - by still my ba - by true._____

Starlight Express

Music by Andrew Lloyd Webber
Lyrics by Richard Stilgoe

Voice: **Piano**
Rhythm: **Ballad**
Tempo: **Quite slow** ♩ = 96

When your good - nights have been said,___ and you are

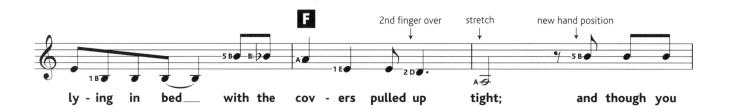

ly - ing in bed___ with the cov - ers pulled up tight; and though you

count ev - 'ry sheep,___ you get the feel - ing that sleep is gon - na

stay a - way to - night._____ That's when you hear it

com - ing, that is when you hear the hum - ming of the

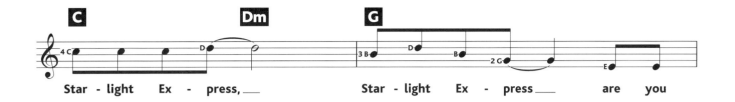

Star - light Ex - press, ___ Star - light Ex - press ___ are you

new hand position

real, ___ yes or no? Star - light Ex - press, ___

stretch

an - swer me yes, ___ I don't want you to go.

new hand position

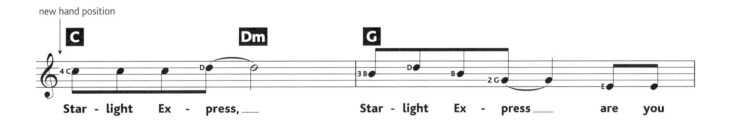

Star - light Ex - press, ___ Star - light Ex - press ___ are you

real, ___ yes or no? Star - light Ex - press, ___

stretch

an - swer me yes, ___ I don't want you to go.

The Time Warp

Words & Music by Richard O'Brien

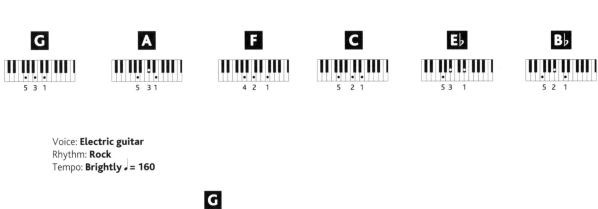

Voice: **Electric guitar**
Rhythm: **Rock**
Tempo: **Brightly** ♩ = 160

It's as-tound-ing,   time is

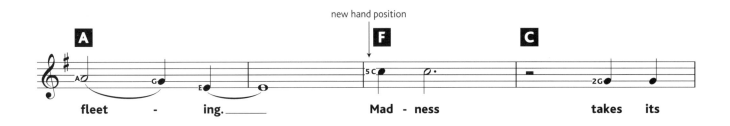

fleet-ing. _____   Mad-ness   takes its

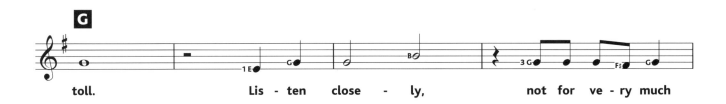

toll.   Lis-ten close-ly,   not for ve-ry much

long-er,   I've got to keep _____ con-

-trol. _____   I re-mem-ber _____

do - ing   the   time   warp, _____

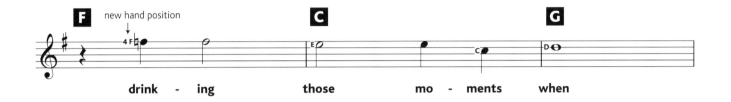

drink - ing   those   mo - ments   when

the   black - ness   hit   me. ____   And   the   world   would   be

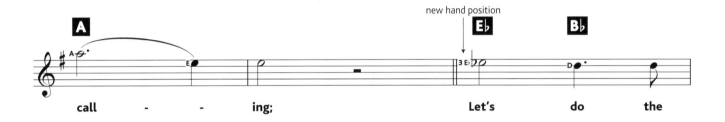

call - - ing;   Let's   do   the

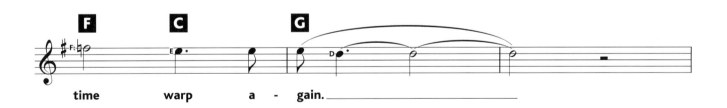

time   warp   a - gain. _____

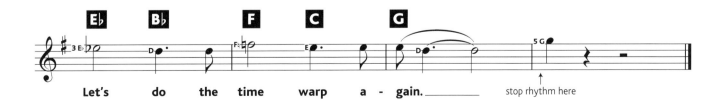

Let's   do   the   time   warp   a - gain. _____

stop rhythm here

You'll Never Walk Alone

Words by Oscar Hammerstein II
Music by Richard Rodgers

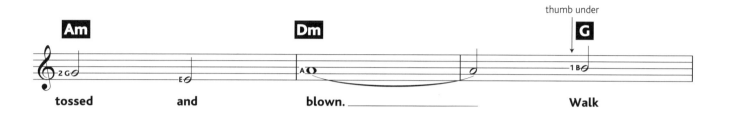

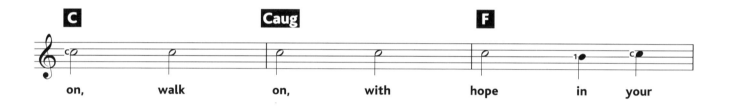

39

Willkommen

Words by Fred Ebb
Music by John Kander

1 2 3 4 5 6 7 8 9